BT

ACC. No: 05023393

Original Korean text by Ah-hae Yun
Illustrations by Mia Shim
Korean edition © Aram Publishing

This English edition published by big & SMALL in 2015
by arrangement with Aram Publishing
English text edited by Joy Cowley
English edition © big & SMALL 2015

All rights reserved

ISBN: 978-1-925234-12-1

Printed in Korea

Princess Star

Written by Ah-hae Yun
Illustrated by Mia Shim
Edited by Joy Cowley

Princess Star likes stars.
She draws stars every day.

"It's time to study numbers,"
says her teacher.

The princess frowns.
"I hate numbers.
I will change all numbers
into beautiful stars!"

"The numbers on the clock
will be yellow stars!"

"Very good!"

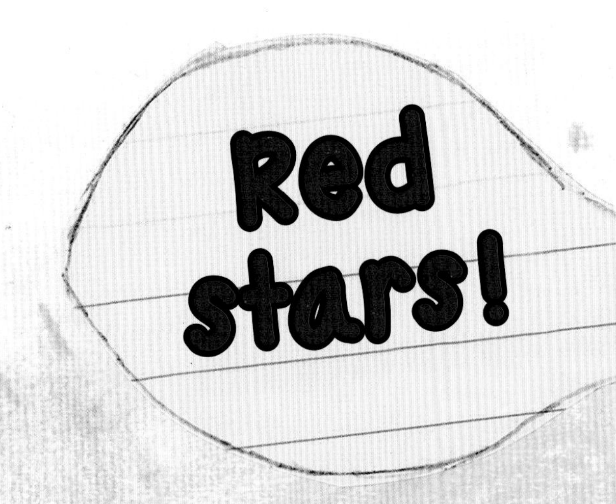

"The numbers on the calendar will be red stars!"

"Wonderful!"

"The numbers on the phone
will be green stars!"

"This is fantastic!"

"The numbers on the lift
will be sparkling stars!"

"I like it! I like it!"

"I'm hungry!" says the princess.
"It must be time to eat.
What time is it now?"

But no one can answer.
There are no numbers
on the clock.

The princess says,
“I can still eat without a clock.
What level is the restaurant?”

But no one can press the button.
There are no numbers on the pad
for the lift.

“My teacher will know,” she says.
“I’ll call him and tell him to come here.”

But she can’t call on the phone
because there are no numbers.

The princess is hungry
and she has tears in her eyes.

Her teacher appears and says,
"In a few days, I want to watch the stars
in the sky, but I cannot tell what day it is
on the calendar."

The princess bursts into sobs.
She realises they need numbers
on the clock, the lift, the phone
and the calendar.

Green

What happens next?
Princess Star still likes stars,
but now she also likes numbers.

Princess Star Likes Stars

Princess Star changed all numbers into stars.
What were those numbers before the change?

Clock
Telephone

Let's Do It Together!

Let's find numbers in streets, supermarkets, at home and in banks.

Number to show the amount of milk

Number on a waiting ticket at a bank

12 1 2 3 4 5 6 7 8 9 10 11
1 2 3
4 5 6
7 8 9
* 0 #

5
10
4
9
2
7
1
6

0 1 2 3 4 5 6 7 8 9

0 1 2 3 4 5 6 7 8 9 10